All invertebrates are unique, but octopuses are among the most unusual and intelligent. They can change their shape and behavior to camouflage themselves. They can unscrew jar lids to reach food inside. They may even be able to dream!

Shrimp, Shrimp, Cuttlefish! © 2020 Audrey Sauble
Published by Larch Books
www.LarchBooks.com

ISBN: 978-1-946748-13-3

Text and illustrations by Audrey Sauble
Cover design by Alaina Arp and Audrey Sauble
Editor: Mary Hake

Author's Note

The beach is one of my favorite places to explore. The shore changes from day to day, and there is always something new to discover. In this book, you will learn about many animals you may find next time you visit.

Please remember that many things you find at the beach are part of the ocean's life cycle. Crabs and other animals eat old bits of seaweed. Other animals reuse empty shells as homes. Unused shells break down into nutrients and sand.

Just like any other natural area you visit, the best rule for protecting beaches is to take only photographs and leave only footprints. There are still plenty of ways to explore the beach without collecting shells, as you will find out in this book.

Featuring:

Octopuses	Sea Anemones
Vampire Squid	Coral Reefs
Cuttlefish	Shrimp
Sand Dollars	Hermit Crabs
Sea Stars	Lobsters
Sea Cucumbers	Barnacles
Sea Slugs	Sponges
Chitons	Jellyfish
Clams	Sea Spiders
Sea Squirts	And more!

Note: some activities in this book require scissors or suggest outdoor play. Adult supervision is recommended as appropriate.

Like octopuses, cuttlefish are cephalopods. Cuttlefish are also extremely clever, just like an octopus. Scientists have found that cuttlefish can learn to escape from mazes. They can also tell the difference between four shrimp and five shrimp.

Scientists sometimes use mazes when they study animals. Mazes can test how different animals explore and remember a place. Can you help this cuttlefish find its way through the maze below to reach the shrimp at the other end?

When you're done, try creating your own maze using chalk, boxes, a ball of string, or other materials.

Vampire squid might look and sound scary—they have spines on their arms and glowing blue spots on the tips of their arms. They're not dangerous, though. They're less than a foot long, and they eat food scraps known as marine snow.

A Finger-Puppet Squid

Despite their name, vampire squid are not squid. A true squid has eight arms and two extra-long tentacles for catching fish. Vampire squid have eight arms and two long, thread-like filaments instead. (Octopuses have eight arms and zero tentacles.)

Follow these instructions to make your own squid—or vampire squid.

Supplies:

- Cardboard tube
- Paper
- Thread, or yarn,
- Tape, glue, and scissors

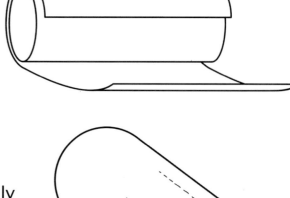

Measure the length of the cardboard tube. Cut a strip of paper as wide as the tube is long. Wrap the paper around the tube and glue it in place.

At one end of the tube, make eight small marks spaced evenly around the edge of the tube. Carefully cut from these marks halfway up the tube. Bend these eight legs out to create an octopus shape.

To turn this puppet into a squid, cut a long piece of yarn or use a pipe cleaner and fold it in half. Tape the yarn or pipe cleaner inside the squid to make its tentacles. (For a vampire squid, use a long piece of thread instead.)

Shape the squid's head by folding the top of the tube in on two sides. This will create triangles on the opposite sides. Pinch these triangles together and tape the top together. Finally, draw eyes on your squid, and make up a story for your new finger puppet.

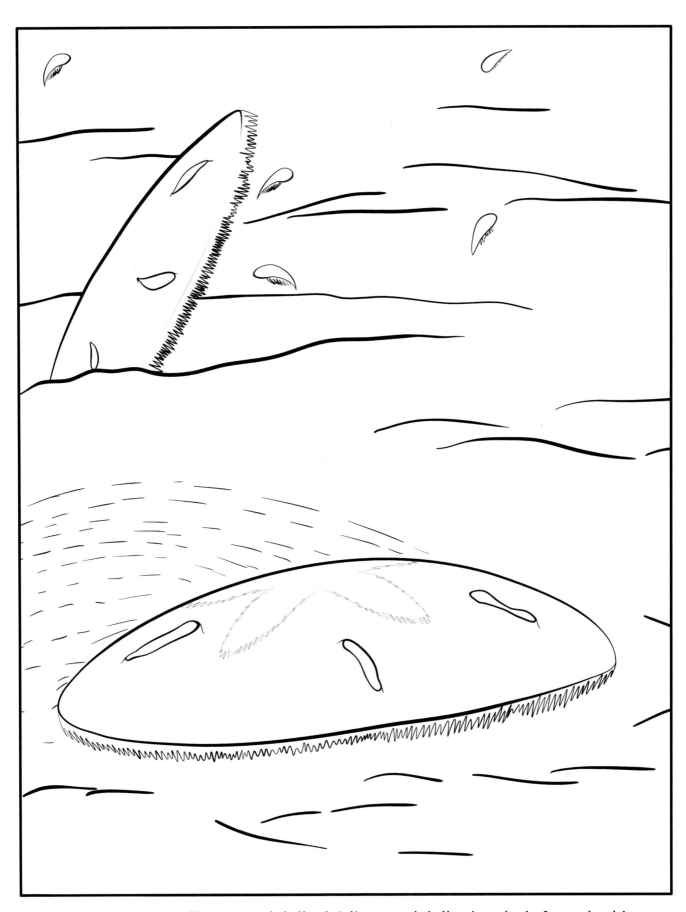

Have you ever seen a living sand dollar? A live sand dollar is a dark, furry-looking animal with colors ranging from greenish-brown to purple. Their "fur" is tiny spines they use to trap food or to creep along the ocean floor.

Sea Hedgehogs?

Did you know? Sea urchins are really "sea hedgehogs." The word "urchin" was originally used as a name for hedgehogs. A sand dollar is a type of sea urchin, but its spines are much shorter than a spiny sea urchin's spines. You can make a spiny sea urchin using a lump of clay and some sticks.

Supplies:

- Clay or play dough
- Small twigs, pine needles, or toothpicks

Start by rolling out a small lump of clay. It should be large enough to fill your hand, but not too large. Shape it into a ball. Then flatten the lower half of your ball against the table so that it doesn't roll around.

If you want, you can paint the sticks to make the sea urchin more colorful—just make sure to let them dry before you assemble your sculpture. Then, poke the sticks into the clay for the sea urchin's needles. Be sure to fill all the edges evenly.

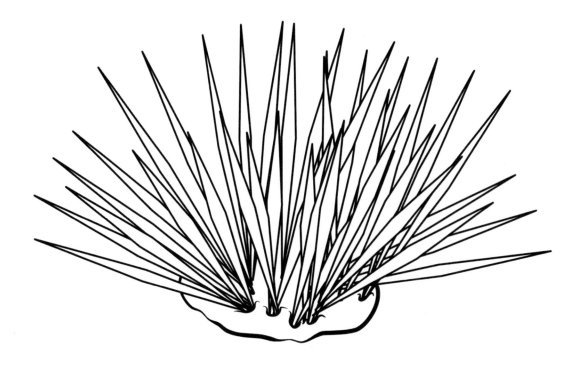

Did you know that sea stars can push their stomachs out through their mouth? When they eat shellfish, they pry the shells open just a crack. Then they slide their stomach through the crack to digest and absorb the mollusk inside its own shell.

Sea Star Circles

Many animals have bilateral symmetry. This is a fancy way of saying that they have two (bi-) matching sides (lateral). If you draw a person and then draw a line straight through their body from their nose to their toes, that person will have the same things on both sides of the line—one ear on each side, one arm on each side, and one leg on each side. This is bilateral symmetry.

Sea stars and jellyfish have radial symmetry. Instead of two matching sides, their bodies have a repeating pattern in a circle, like the spokes of a wheel.

To see how this works, trace this image five times on a separate piece of paper. Cut out the five shapes, and glue them together, one on top of another, following the images below. You've made your very own sea star.

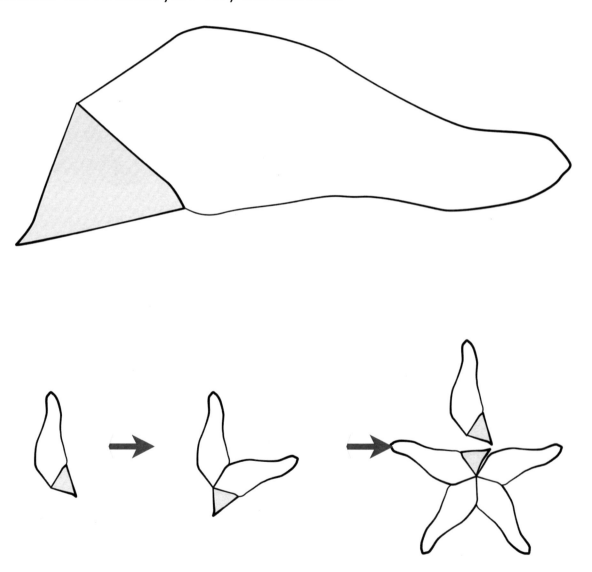

Some sea stars have ten legs, and others have even more. How would you draw one of these sea stars? Could you make a sea star using play dough or clay?

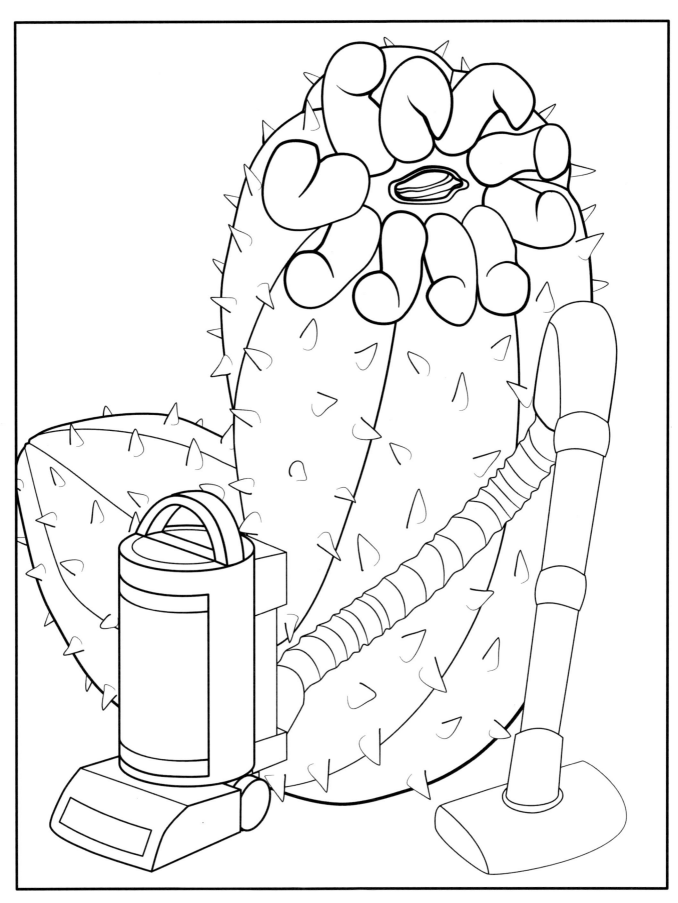

Do sea cucumbers sound small and boring? Most are only a few inches long, but some can be more than six feet long. Sea cucumbers spend their day vacuuming up food bits from the ocean floor—rather like worms in a garden.

Eggshell Science

Note: this experiment will take two to five days.

Coral skeletons are made of calcium carbonate, the same material found in eggshells. To get this material, coral needs to absorb it from seawater.

That's where sea cucumbers become sea heroes.

Sea cucumbers chomp up bits of shells and broken coral containing calcium carbonate, along with algae, sand, and other debris. The acid in their digestive tracts dissolves the calcium carbonate, releasing it back into the water for corals to use. As they do this, the sea cucumbers also make the water around them less acidic, protecting coral from acid compounds that might damage their skeletons.

You can observe this process using vinegar and leftover eggshells.

Start by measuring one cup of vinegar (an acid) into a cup or a jar. Crush up a couple of eggshells (calcium carbonate) and drop them into the vinegar.

Leave the jar somewhere safe for a few days, checking it occasionally to see how the eggshells are changing.

After a few days, most of the eggshells should have dissolved into the vinegar. You can test this change using baking soda. ***This might get messy, so move the experiment to a large sink or take it outside.***

Measure out a second cup of vinegar into a fresh jar. Add one tablespoon of baking soda into the fresh vinegar. Note what happens. Now add one tablespoon of baking soda to the eggshell solution. What happens this time?

Reaction #1:_____

Reaction #2:_____

What do you think will happen if you try this experiment again, but change the amount of vinegar, eggshell, or baking soda? Can you think of other experiments to try using eggshells?

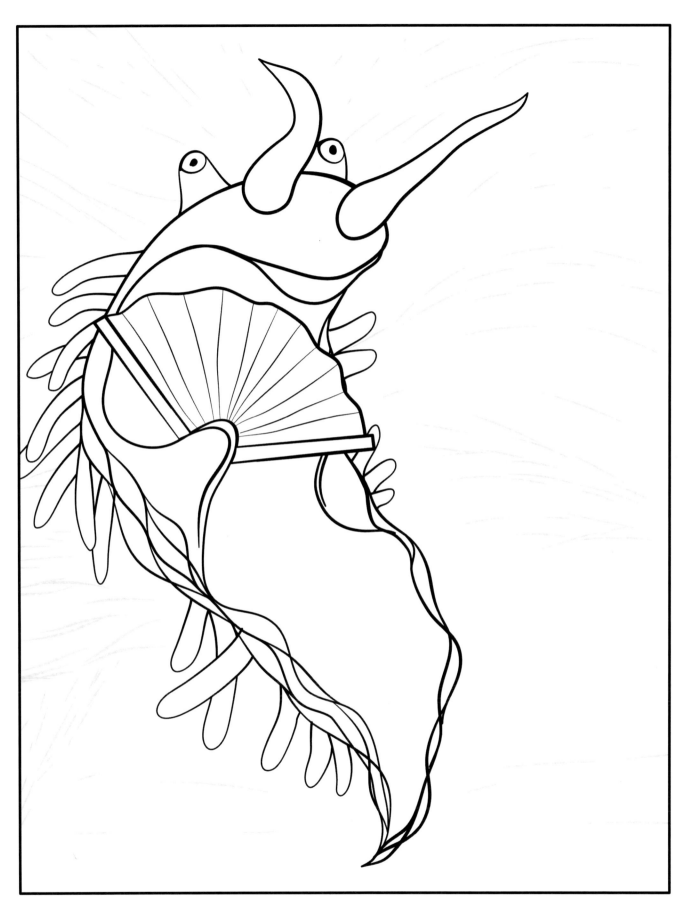

Nudibranchs, a family of sea slugs, are often brightly colored, with rows of frills along their backs or sides. These frills aren't just for show, however. Some of them act as gills, absorbing oxygen from the water, while others detect important scents.

Compared with land-dwelling slugs, sea slugs are wild and colorful. They belong to the scientific class gastropod (or stomach-footed), but some particularly unique, nearly transparent sea slugs belong to a group called pteropods (or wing-footed). These sea slugs are known as sea angels. Connect the dots below to find out why.

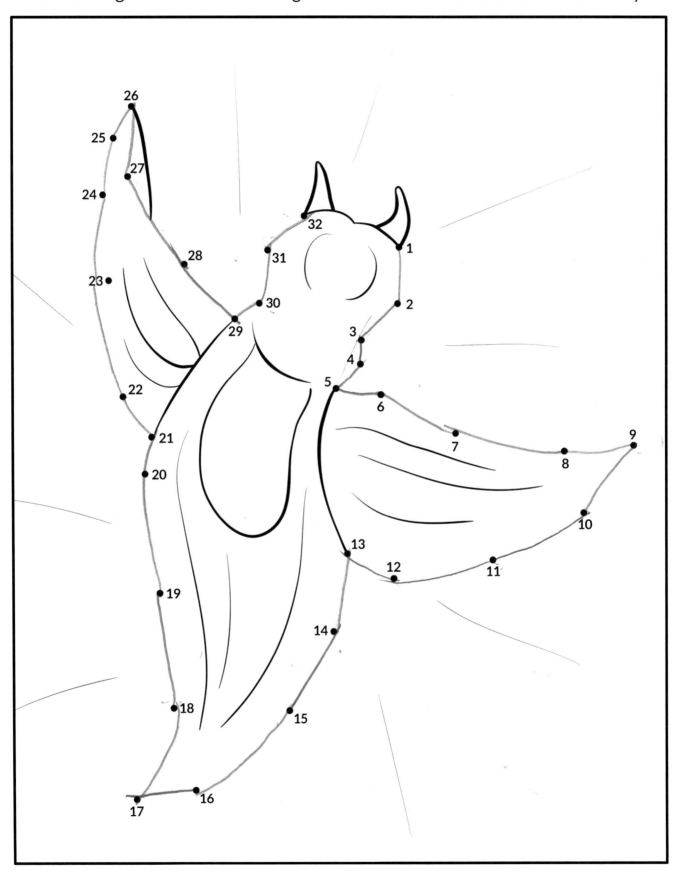

Elysia chlorotica is a rather unusual animal. Like other sea slugs, it feeds on algae. However, it can also absorb chloroplasts from the algae into its cells, where it uses the chloroplasts to produce energy from sunlight like a plant does.

After you color the picture on the other side of this page, use a pair of scissors to cut out the rectangles above. Then turn them over. You have made your own puzzle.

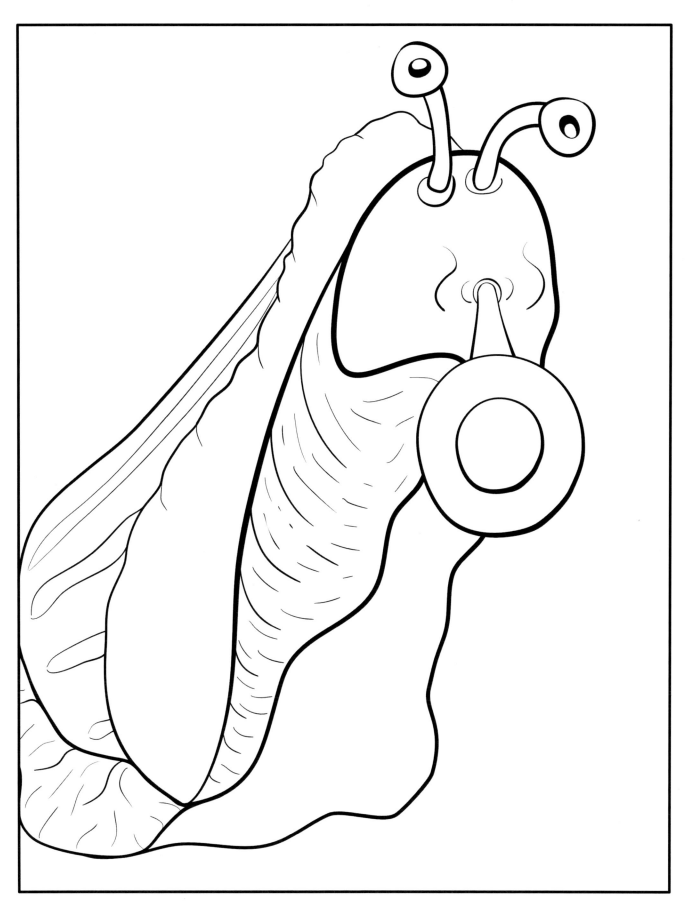

You may have seen conch shells before—they are large and colorful and can be used as musical instruments. The name conch is used for a number of species of large marine snails, relatives of the smaller snails you might find in your garden.

A Melodious Experiment

Movement is a form of energy, and sometimes that energy turns into music. Plucking a guitar's strings, tapping on a drum, or playing a piano all turn energy into music—and so does blowing air through a conch shell.

For this experiment, use a clean narrow-necked bottle, either glass or plastic.

Start by blowing gently across the mouth of the bottle. If you blow at the right angle, you will create a horn-like noise. This noise is created by air vibrations inside the bottle.

Now add an inch of water to the bottle and blow across it. Does the noise change?

If you have several bottles, try adding a different amount of water to each bottle. Can you create musical notes and play a tune with these bottles?

What other ways could you change the air vibrations in a bottle or create other types of musical vibrations?

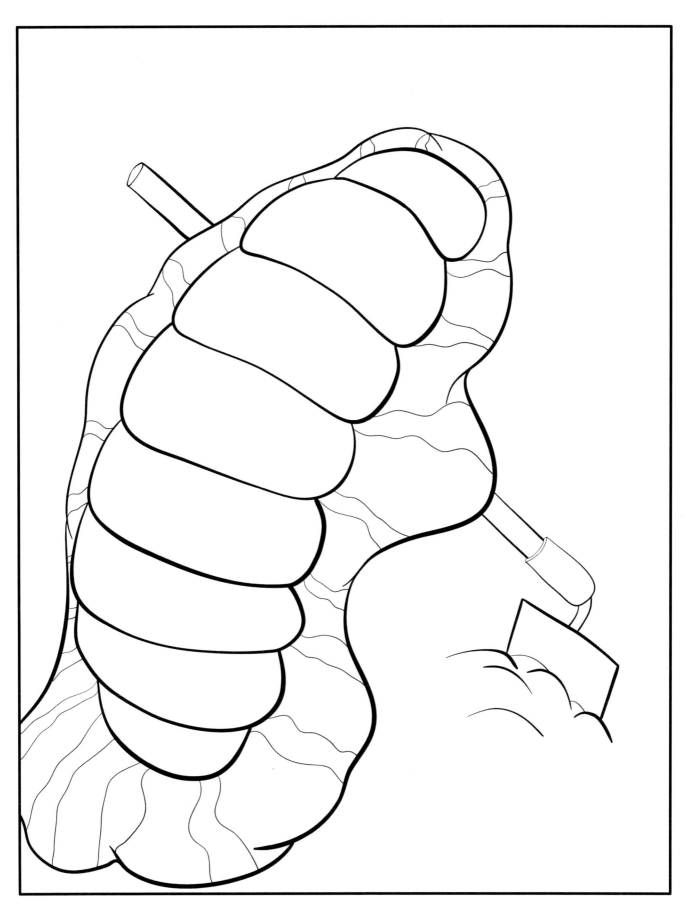

What do you get when you cross a snail with a pill bug? A chiton! Chitons have jointed shells like a pill bug or a trilobite, but they're soft-bodied mollusks similar to a snail, and they slide along rocks, scraping off bits of food to eat.

What's the Difference?

Snails and chitons are both mollusks, and both creep along the ground, scraping up food. But—they have very different shells. For this project, you will compare how they use their shells to protect themselves.

Supplies:

- Cardboard boxes
- Tape and scissors
- Two small blankets

First, roll one blanket up into a loose tube and lay it on the floor. This is your snail. Place a cardboard box on top of the snail.

How much of the snail does the box protect? If a predator comes along, how will the snail be able to hide?

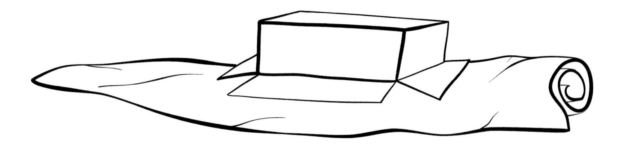

Now cut the other box into eight pieces. They do not have to be the same size, but they should be similar sizes. Fold the edges in slightly, and then tape the cardboard sections together in a row. Spread the second blanket loosely on the floor and place the chiton's plated shell on top of it.

How much of the chiton does this shell protect? Will it respond to a predator the same way as a snail?

Design challenge: Can you adapt the chiton's shell to make a shell you could wear?

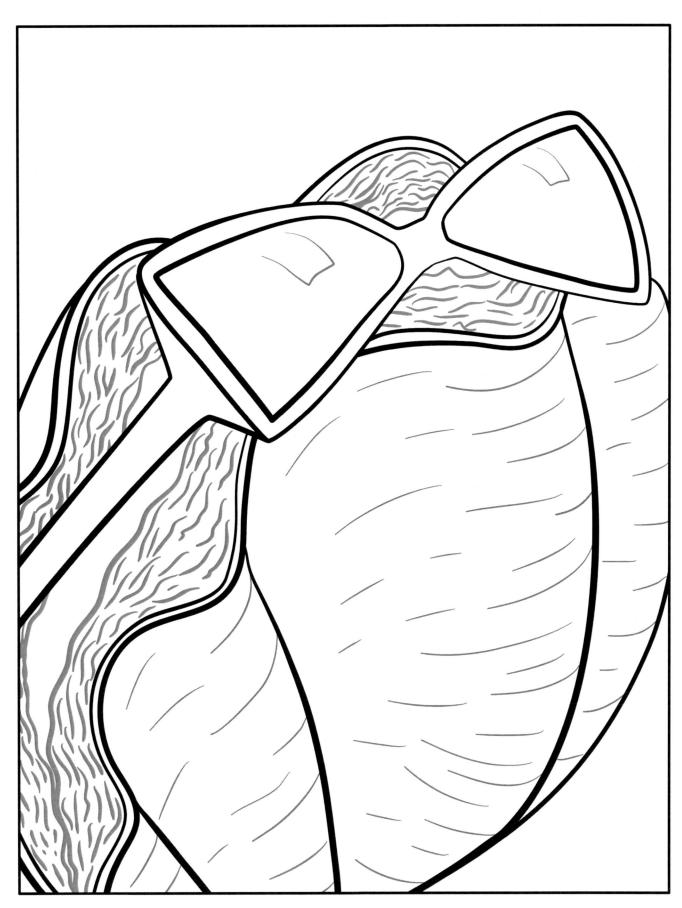

Unlike oysters, mussels, and most other clams, giant clams have eyes. These eyes don't see much—they can only sense light and shadow. However, a giant clam has hundreds of these eyes lining the soft mantle at the edges of their shells.

Build a Clam

Clams are a type of bivalve mollusks. That means they are a soft-body animal like a slug, but they live inside two shells connected by a hinge. Here's how you can create your own clam:

Supplies:

- Two paper plates
- A sheet of paper
- Tissue paper
- Glue
- Markers or crayons

Start by folding the paper in half, creasing it carefully. Cut along the crease to create two sections. Fold one of these sections in half again.

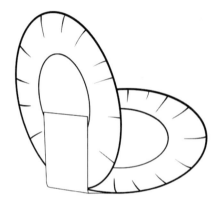

Glue one plate to one half of the paper as shown. Glue the other plate to the other end of the same piece of paper. This creates a hinged shell. Test it by opening and closing the shell.

Fold the tissue paper in half, and then in half again until it is just larger than one of the plates. Lay it on top of one plate, with the folded edge opposite the paper hinge. Shape it to fit inside the plates, then glue it to the bottom plate.

Wait for the glue to set, before spreading fresh glue on the top plate and pressing that plate onto the paper.

Once the glue is dry, test your clam. It should open slightly, but the clam's tissue-paper "muscles" should keep it from opening all the way.

Use the markers or crayons to decorate your clam. Be sure to add blue dots for eyes along the edges of the tissue paper.

Scallops don't have legs, but they still get about. Most scallops can "swim" by pulling water into their shells, and then squirting it out again in a rapid jet. This pushes the scallop forward across the ocean floor, helping it escape from predators.

Seashells by the Seashore

Each beach is a unique place. Some have rocks and tide pools. Some have a long, sandy shoreline.

At some beaches, you might find dozens of mussel shells. At others, you might find only clam shells. If you visit after a storm, you might find sand dollar skeletons, or snail shells. Use this handy chart to track which shells and other sea animals are most common at your favorite beach. (If you can't visit a beach, find some books about the ocean, and chart the types of shells shown in those books.)

Beach name: _____ Date: _____

Clam shells															
Mussel shells															
Scallop shells															
Snail shells															
Tusk shells															
Cone shells															
Cowrie shells															
Tube shells															
Sand dollars															
Sea stars															
Crabs															

(If you want to try this activity multiple times, be sure to copy this page before using it, or draw your own chart on a separate piece of paper.

Is plankton a plant or an animal? Neither? Both? Plankton species include everything from bacteria to single-celled algae to crab larvae. Their common trait isn't their species but their tendency to drift through the water, rather than swim.

The Breakfast Food of Giants

A blue whale, the largest animal in the world, eats one of the smallest animals in the world—krill! Krill grow between one-half inch and four inches long, so they are relatively large for plankton, but still tiny compared with a blue whale.

Can you help this krill escape from the blue whale's baleen maze?

Sea squirts are unusual creatures that start out in life as tiny fishlike plankton. Then they grow up, anchor themselves to a rock, and turn into spongy blobs that filter food particles from the water.

Adult sea squirts are strange animals that look more like a plant than an animal. They don't even have a proper brain, but they do have a rudimentary spinal cord. (This spinal cord means they are more closely related to animals with a vertebrate than they are to true invertebrates like snails and crabs.)

Sea squirts also have another important organ that some other animals like jellyfish and coral lack. Use the numbers as a guide to color the picture below and find what out what this organ is.

1 = brown   2 = pink   3 = red   4 = purple   5 = yellow   6 = blue

Unlike a human heart, a sea squirt's heart is just a simple tube, but it does mean the sea squirt is definitely an animal, not a plant.

A horde of animals, packed together, snatching up food with their tentacles? It sounds scary, but bryozoans are tiny. A massive colony looks rather like a patch of moss. These colonies eat tiny particles of food that they filter from the water.

Art Challenge

Artists sometimes practice by drawing the same things over and over. This helps them to focus on simple lines, curves, and shapes. It can also be a relaxing way to doodle. Can you fill this entire square with the same shape? It could be a circle, a square, a diamond, or a colony of squiggly bryozoans. Focus on filling the whole space, but make sure you draw a mix of big and small shapes.

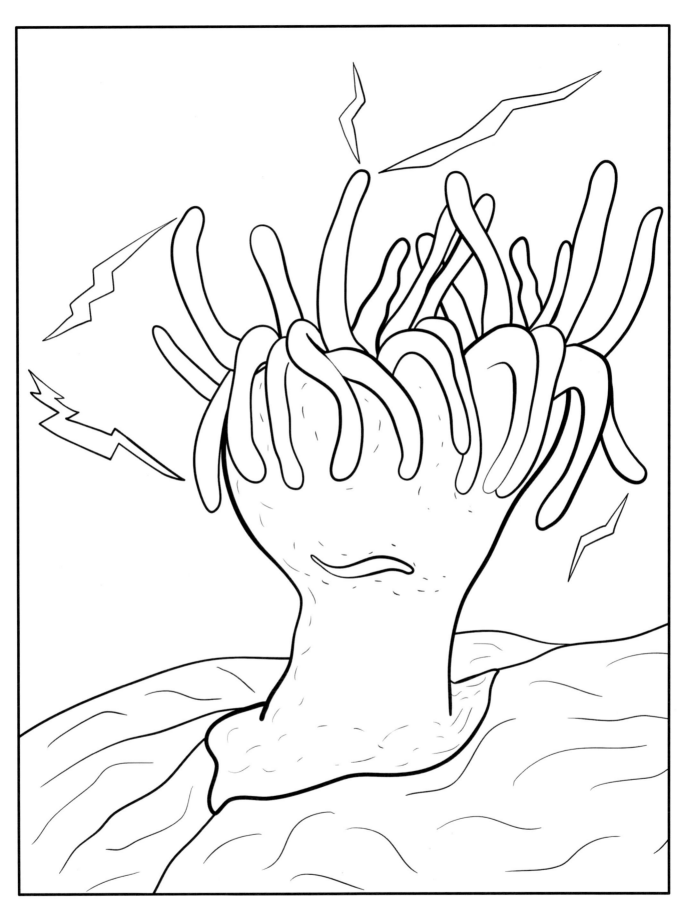

Sea anemones can be fluorescent green, bright pink, or any number of other colors. Sometimes these colors come from tiny single-celled organisms that live inside of the anemones and harvest energy from sunlight.

Drawing an Anemone

Sea anemones come in all sizes, shapes, and colors. The largest known species is more than three feet wide and looks like a thick, shaggy carpet. This sort of anemone is easy to draw by using lots of loose rough bumps to give it texture.

For a taller anemone, you can create some motion by drawing the anemone swaying in the current. Bend your lines in the direction that the anemone is moving. Lightly sketch an oval at the top of the anemone, then draw in the tentacles around this oval. The tentacles are looking for food to catch, so draw them stretching out and sweeping through the water. You may need to erase some edges where the tentacles overlap each other.

Finally, some anemones close into tight balls when they sense danger. This is especially common on rocky shores, when the tide pulls back, and the anemones need to protect themselves from drying out. For this anemone, start by drawing a lumpy ball. Draw a few tentacles peeking out at the top, and add some rough texture to the anemone.

A coral reef is a bustling city, full of fish, crabs, seahorses, sea slugs, and, of course, coral. The coral itself is an apartment building—a house full of tiny rooms for the tiny animals who build the coral with their exoskeletons.

Growing a Colony

Coral starts as a single polyp that anchors to a stone, an old shipwreck, or some other solid bit of ground. Then the single polyp splits into more and more buds, slowly building a massive colony. As each bud matures, it builds a bony structure that gives the coral its shape. The first polyp has just planted itself below—draw the rest of the colony around it to help it grow.

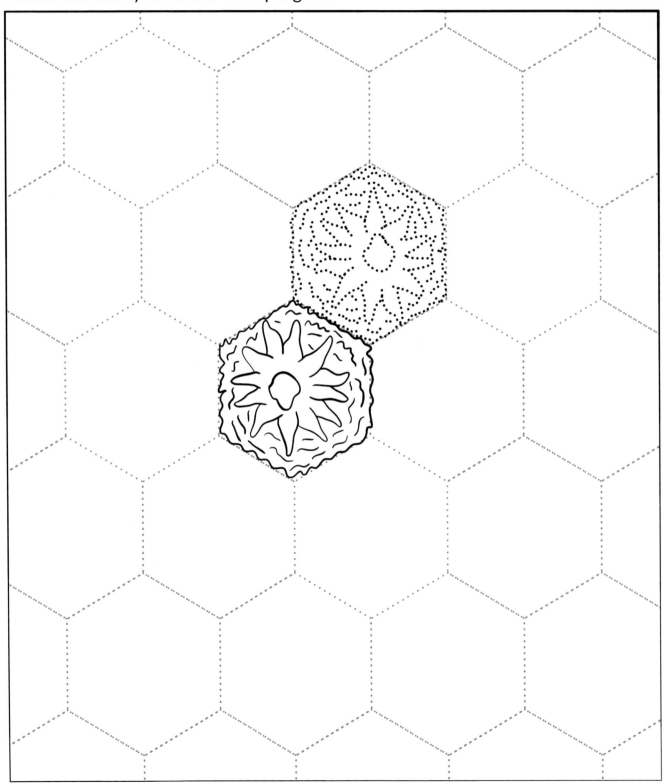

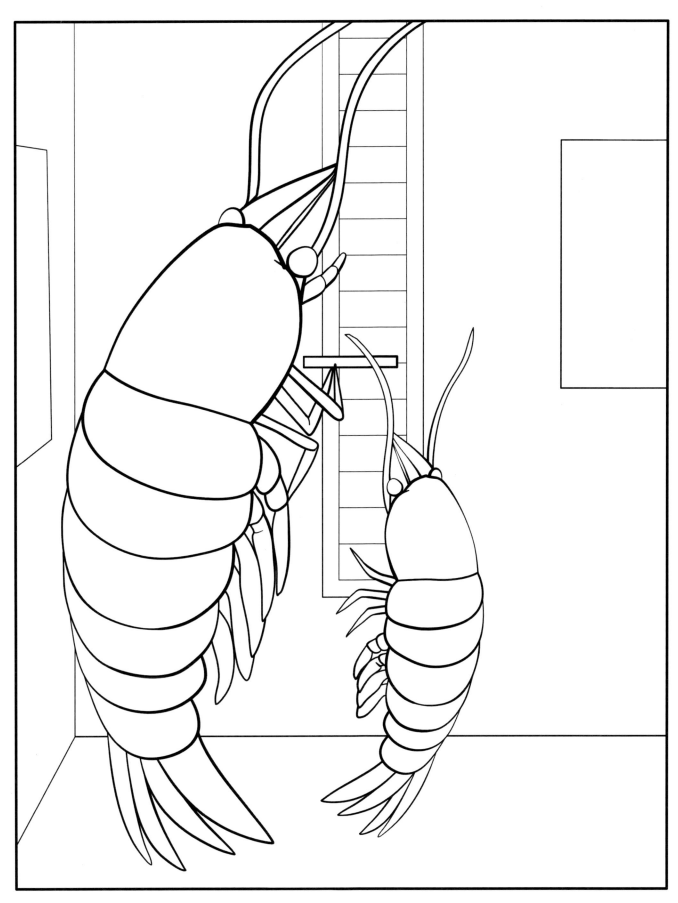

We frequently use the word "shrimp" to mean something small. It's true that many shrimp are small—some species grow to be only an inch long—but other species can weigh up to a pound and grow almost a foot long.

How Do You See?

Many species of animals have unique ways of seeing. Shrimp, crabs, and lobsters all have eyestalks that allow them to move each eye separately and watch the water around them for predators. Bees can see ultraviolet light, which allows them to focus on flowers.

We can't see ultraviolet light or wiggle our eyes to look in all directions, but we have created tools that we use to look at the world in a different way. How many different tools can you think of?

Use the space below to design your own gadget for looking at the world differently. Then see if you can build it! It could be as simple rolling up a piece of paper for a spyglass, or it could be fancy and elaborate, like sci-fi goggles that let you see behind yourself.

Possible answers: binoculars, telescopes, microscopes, cameras, periscopes, night vision goggles, UV spectrometers, eyeglasses, sunglasses, and more.

Hermit crabs do not have hard shells to protect their entire body, so they live inside empty seashells, especially snail shells. These recycled homes protect the crabs' soft tails, but they must trade the shells for larger ones as they grow.

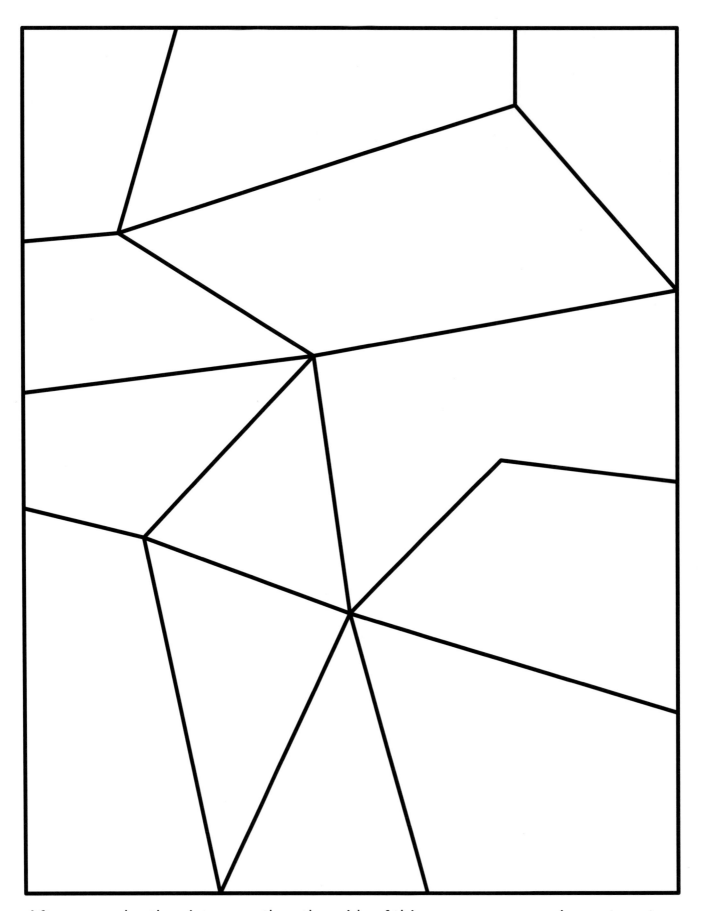

After you color the picture on the other side of this page, use your scissors to cut out the shapes above. Then turn them over. You have made your own puzzle.

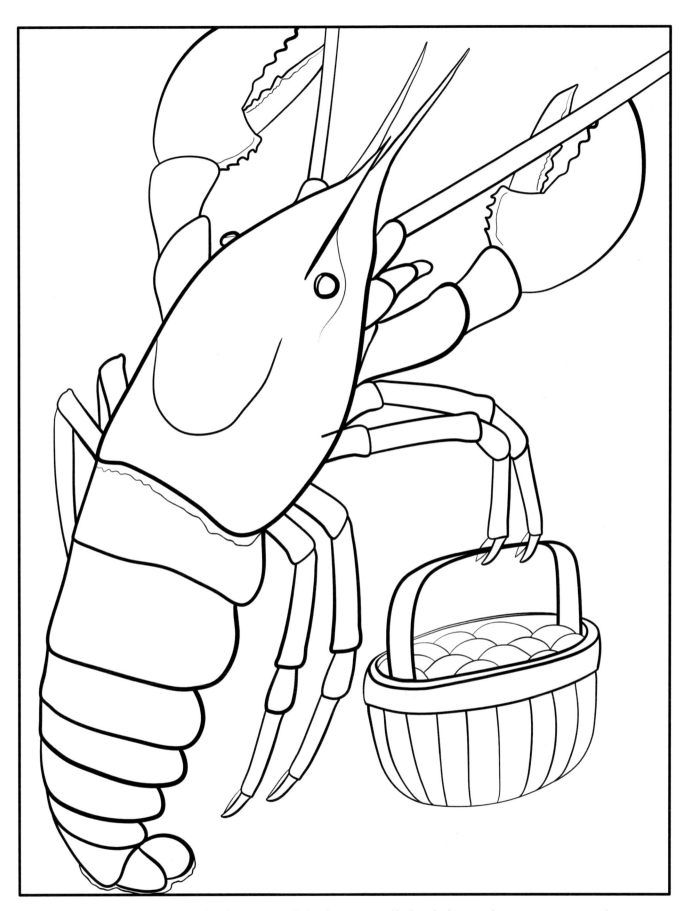

Lobster mothers carry their eggs with them until the lobster larvae are ready to hatch. Lobsters don't have baskets to keep their eggs in, though. How do these mothers carry their thousands of eggs? Underneath their tails!

Like most animals, lobsters have bilateral symmetry. If you look straight down at one and draw an imaginary line from its head to its tail, the two sides will mirror each other exactly. Sometimes, each half will be an entirely different color.

Use the grid below to help you draw the other half of this lobster.

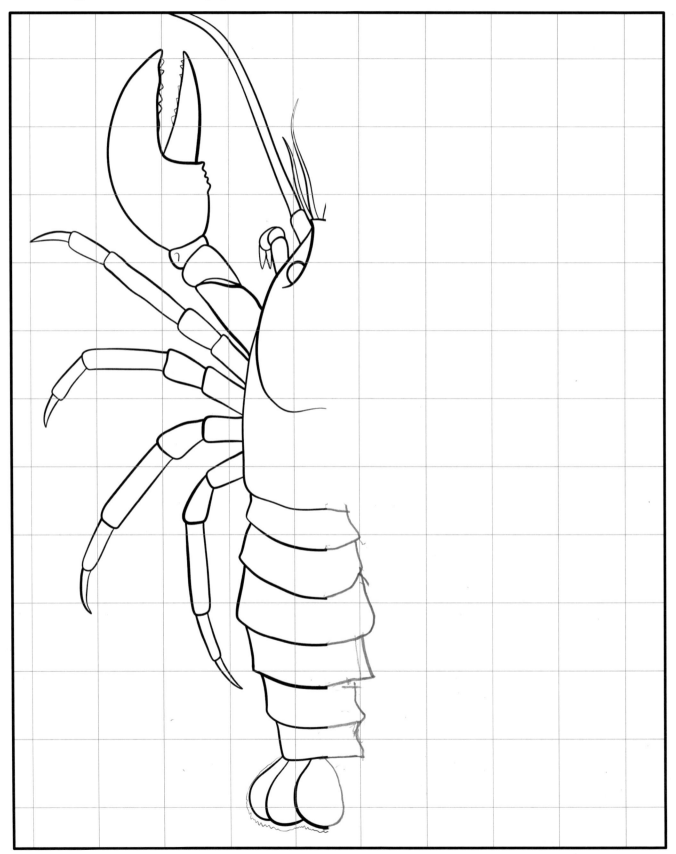

Decorator crabs all have the same habit—dressing up their shells with algae, mossy material, or even anemones. Like all crabs, these crabs shed their shells as they grow, but they often reattach their old decorations to their new shells.

Decorator crabs aren't trying to look fancy. They use their decorating skills to camouflage themselves and hide from predators. With a tuft of algae growing on their back, they can blend into the rest of the scenery. Connect the dots in the picture below to see how well this crab stays hidden.

Barnacles live life upside down. As babies, they swim in the ocean like tiny fish. When they grow up, they glue their head to a rock, build a shell around themselves, and use their frilly feet to sweep food into their mouth.

A Traveler's Life?

What can journey around the world, but never leave its home? A barnacle! (Well, yes . . . turtles too.) Most of the time, barnacles fasten onto stationary objects such as rocks or boat docks. Sometimes, though, they fasten onto whales or the hull of a ship. Then they hitch a ride on someone else's adventures.

Draw a picture of something these barnacles might see on their journey. Just remember—barnacles must stay underwater to survive, so their view of the ocean might be upside down.

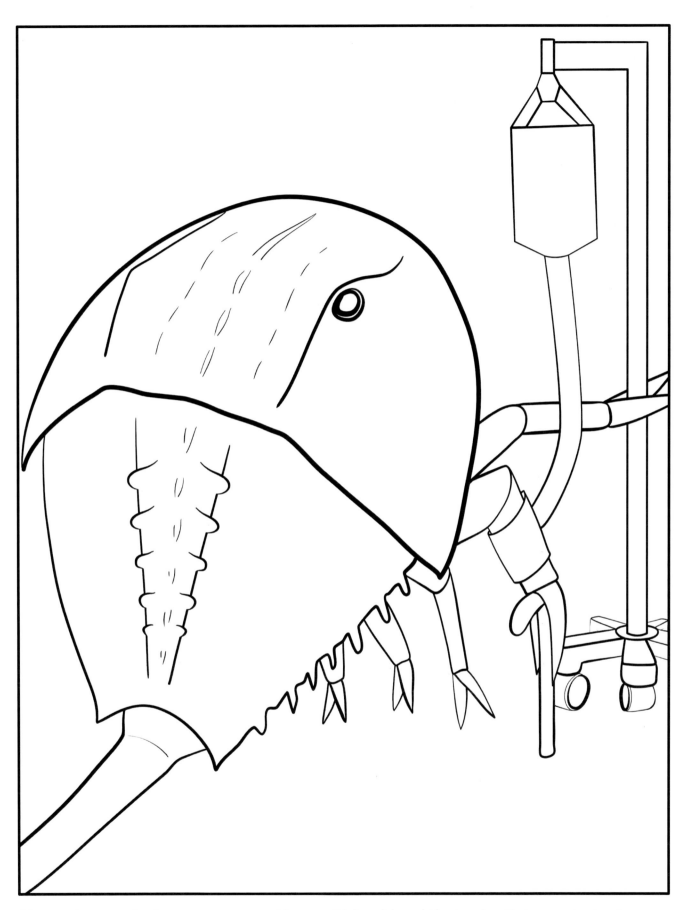

Horseshoe crabs have an unusual type of blue blood that scientists use to test drugs for certain toxins. This protects humans, but it also hurts a lot of horseshoe crabs, so scientists are working to find artificial alternatives to replace this test.

The Same and Different

While horseshoe crabs share their name with hermit crabs and other crabs, they are not crustaceans. Instead, these "crabs" are related to arachnids (spiders, ticks, and scorpions). Look at the pictures below and see if you can spot some of the similarities and differences between horseshoe crabs and spiders.

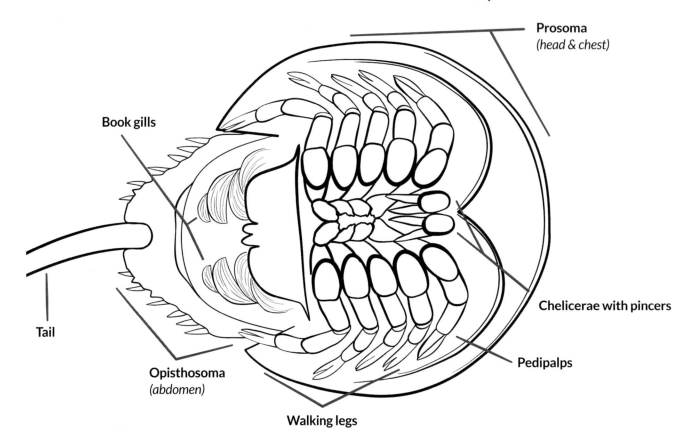

Prosoma
(head & chest)

Book gills

Tail

Opisthosoma
(abdomen)

Walking legs

Chelicerae with pincers

Pedipalps

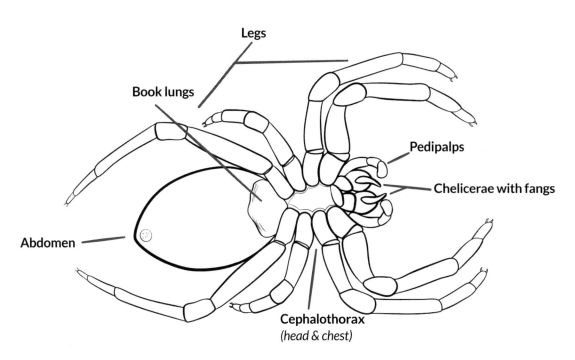

Legs

Book lungs

Abdomen

Pedipalps

Chelicerae with fangs

Cephalothorax
(head & chest)

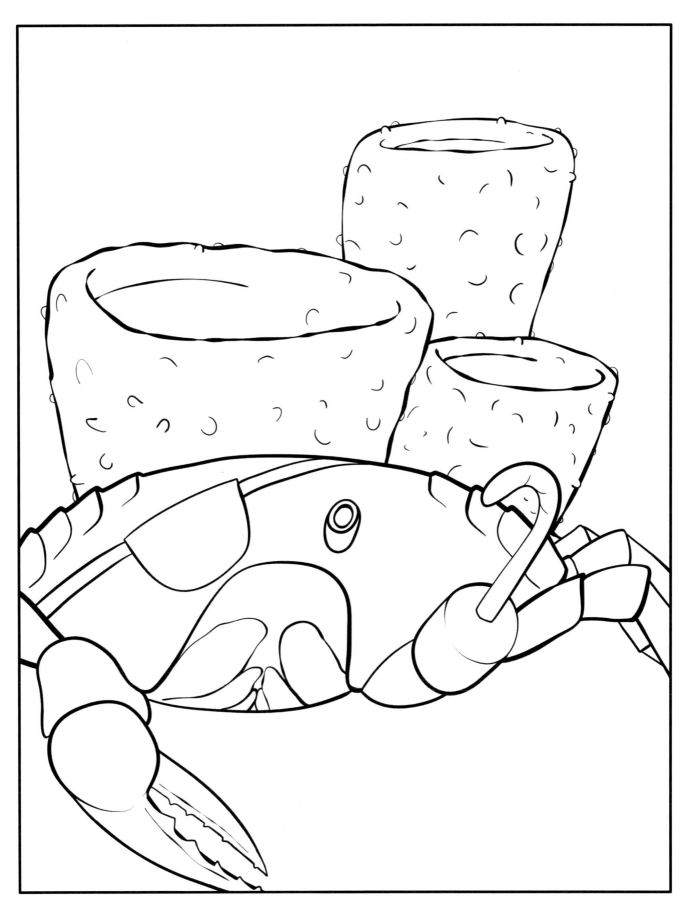

Crabs—along with spiders, insects, and other arthropods—can regrow their legs and claws over time. The missing claw grows back slowly with each molt. As adults, though, crabs eventually stop molting and lose the ability to regrow their claws.

How to Draw a Ghost Crab

A ghost crab gets its name in part from its pale color, which helps these crabs hide in the sand along shorelines around the world. While crabs have strange, awkward bodies, they're fun to draw if you turn their bodies into simple shapes. Plus, ghost crabs have extra-long eyestalks that can give them a lot of personality.

Start by drawing a trapezoid. Round the top and the corners just a bit to give the crab's body a softer shape. Draw two semicircles, overlapping the lower corners of the crab's body. One semicircle should be slightly larger than the other. Draw the main claw section, then finish the claws with the triangular pincer finger.

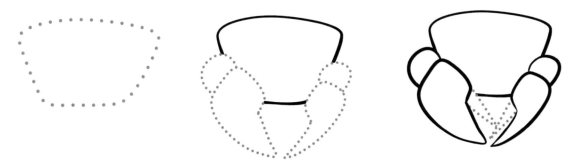

Part of the crab's legs will be hidden behind its claws. Draw a set of parallel lines on each side of the crab's body. Add knees—rounding them at the top and flattening them at the bottom. Draw one more leg section, then finish with a claw-like toe.

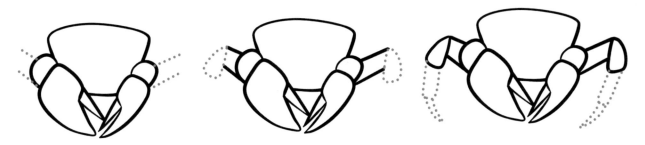

Add two slightly hooked mouth pieces, and two more half-ovals for the crab's eyestalks. On each eyestalk, draw an oval just larger than the eyestalk. Erase any stray lines and draw in thin slits for the crab's pupils. If you want to draw a horned ghost crab, add thin antenna-like stems on top of its eyes.

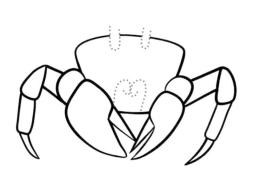

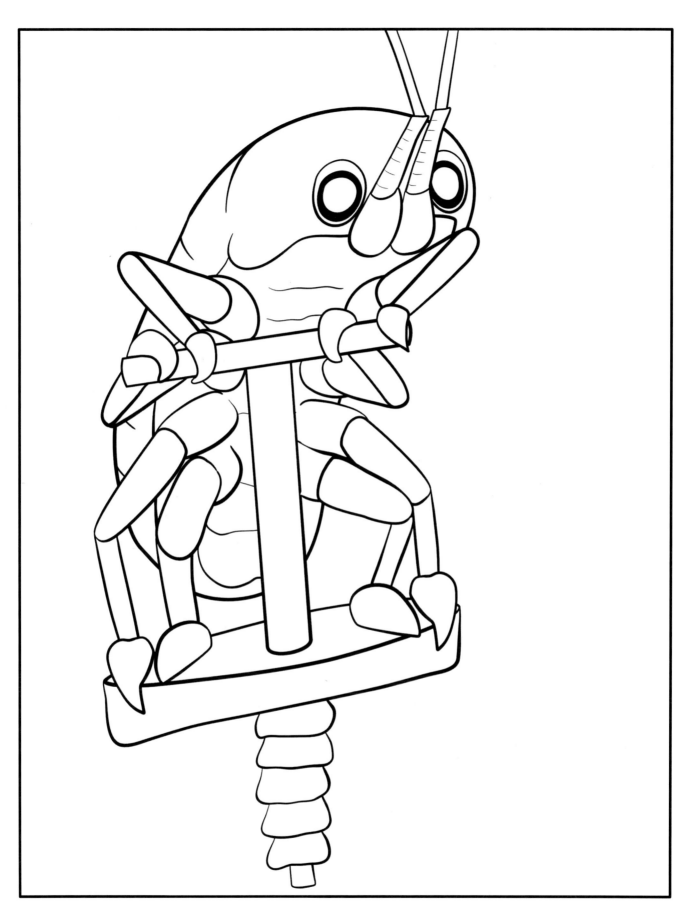

These tiny creatures are sometimes called sand fleas, but only because they can hop like a flea. They don't bite humans or other animals, and they feed on decaying ocean debris, so their other name—sand hoppers—fits them better.

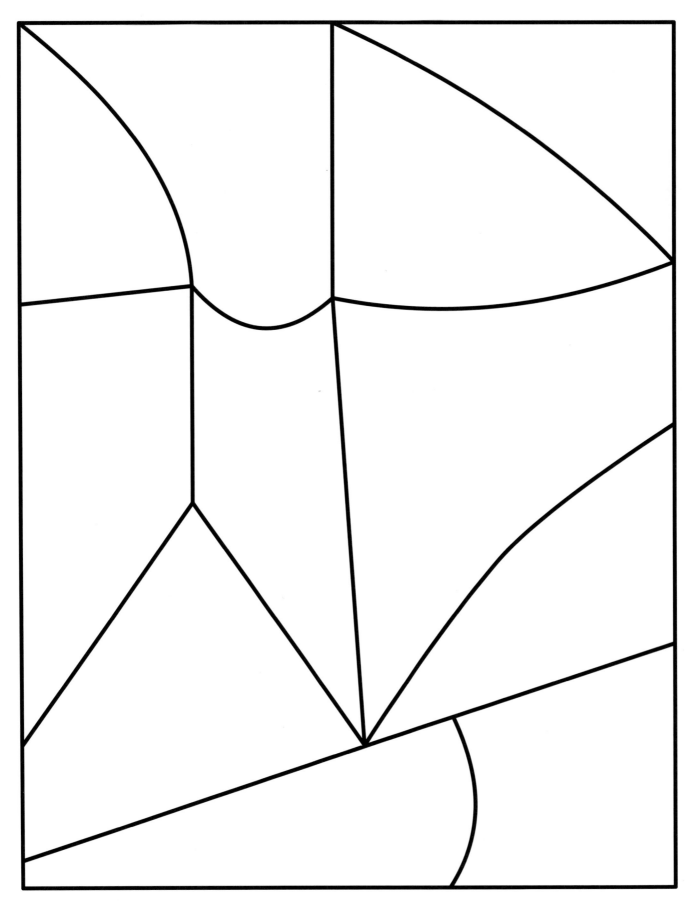

After you color the picture on the other side of this page, use your scissors to cut out the shapes above. Then turn them over. You have made your own puzzle.

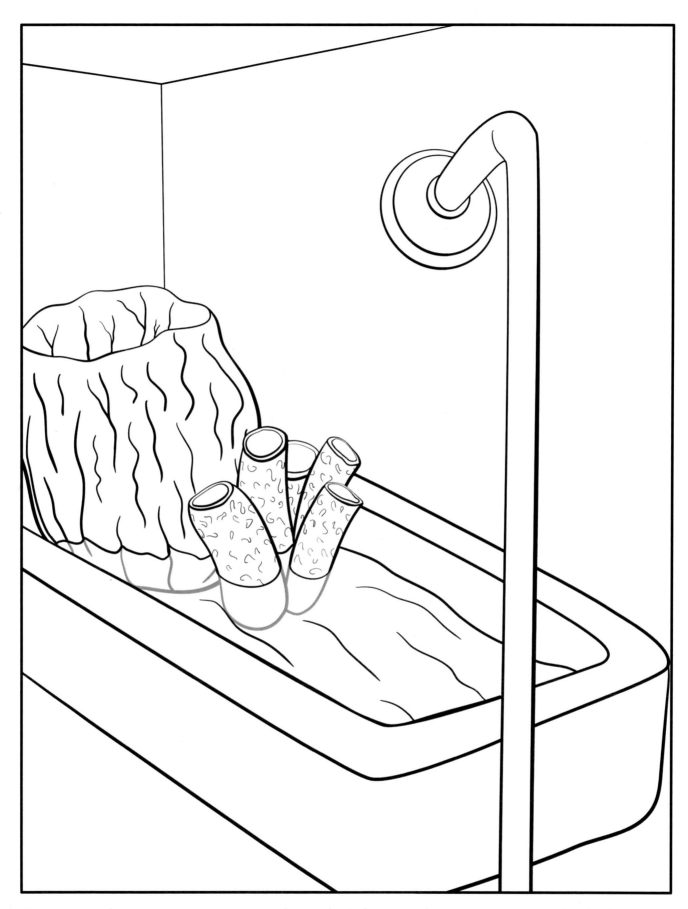

Some people use sea sponges to clean their houses, but sea sponges also help clean the ocean. Sponges filter bits of food from the water and release oxygen, keeping the ocean clean and healthy for other animals.

Sponge Painting

Despite their name, many sponges are rough and firm. Some, though, have soft fibers. These sponges are also very absorbent, and people have used them for cleaning for thousands for years. This has caused some types of sea sponges to be over-harvested, but now you can find artificial sponges made from a wide variety of materials.

You can even find sponge brushes specifically for certain types of painting. If you have one of these brushes, you can use it for this project, or you can use a cleaning sponge—you could even recycle a worn-out sponge and use it for painting.

Supplies:

- Watercolors, acrylic paint, or finger paints
- A sponge brush or general sponge
- Heavy paper or cardstock

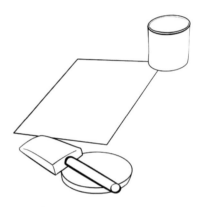

Set up your painting supplies and a container with water for cleaning your sponge. Feel free to sketch out your idea lightly before you start painting, or you can make things up as you go along.

Experiment to see what different kinds of textures you can create. If you soak the sponge with paint, you can fill in the whole area, but if you just tap it gently across the paper, you can create patterns and textures.

You can paint something simple like a fish, or you can try something more complicated like a coral reef.

For a fish, sketch the shape lightly, then paint it using your sponge. Add a strand of seaweed or two so that the fish has a place to hide. Be sure to let the paint dry before layering new colors onto the paper.

For a coral reef, focus on the shape of the coral, not details. Some coral is tall and spiky, while other coral is round or lumpy, or fan shaped. Add a few small fish shadows the background to suggest distance.

Peanut butter and jellyfish? Zookeepers once tried to feed peanut butter to jellyfish—and the jellies ate it! In the wild, though, peanut butter and jellyfish don't mix. Instead, most jellies eat fish, plankton, and other marine animals.

Jellyfish start life as a plantlike creature called a polyp. When a polyp is mature, it sheds tiny disks that grow into jellyfish. The jellyfish, in turn, spawn microscopic larvae that settle to the ocean floor and become polyps.

Cut out these squares and rearrange them to show a jellyfish's life cycle. Then color the picture.

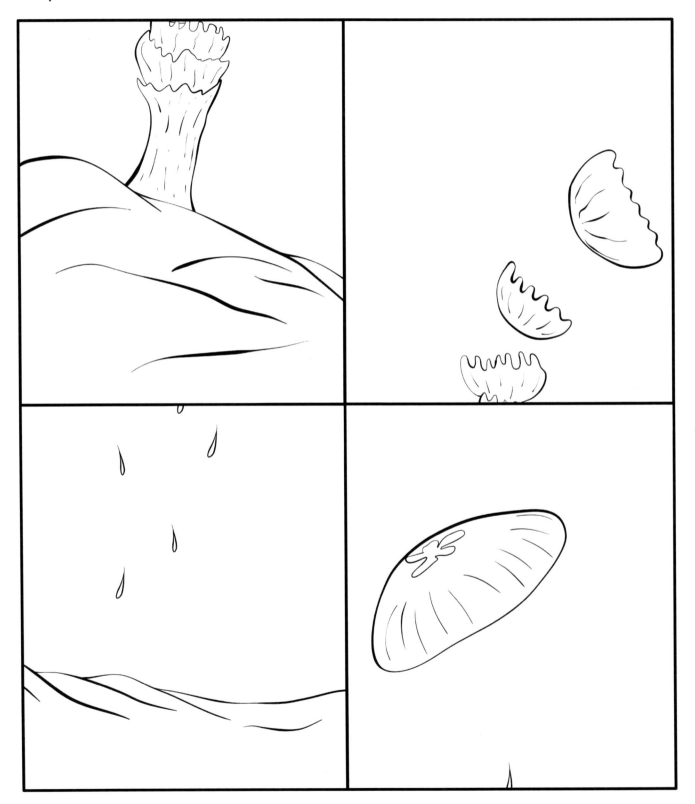

(If you don't want to cut out this page, you can copy or trace it and use that paper instead.)

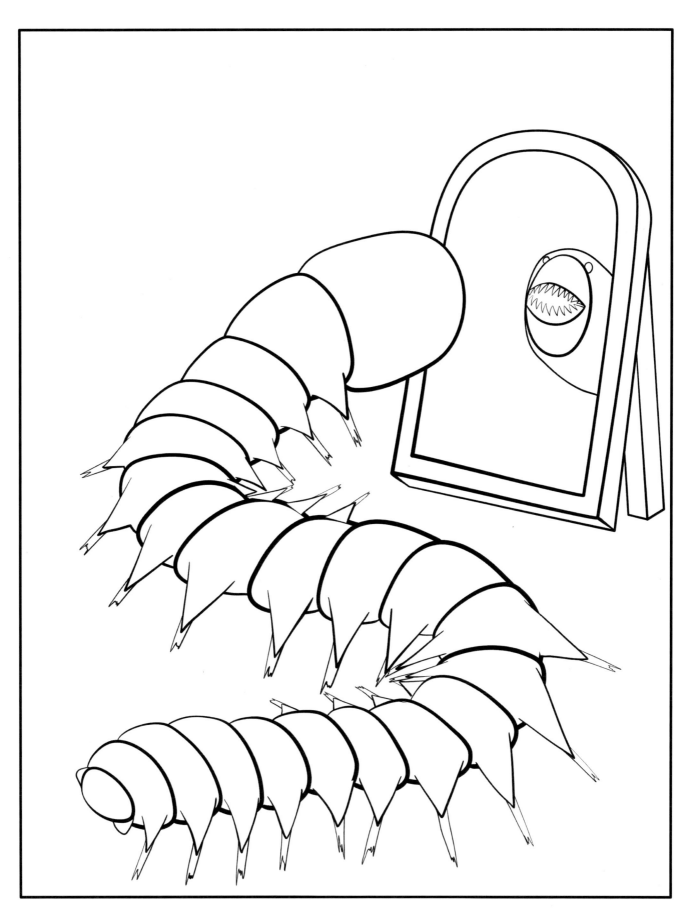

What looks like a centipede but lives in the ocean? A bristle worm! Its "legs" are just fleshy flaps or bristles that the worm might use to crawl, burrow, or swim, or even to sting prey, depending on the species of worm and where it lives.

Soft-Bodied Fossils?

Would you expect a worm to become a fossil? What about a sea star or a jellyfish? These are all soft-bodied animals that decompose quickly after they die. Their bodies rarely survive long enough to fossilize—but sometimes it does happen. Often, this happens when the animal's body is trapped in a layer of sediment, leaving an imprint that hardens as the sediment morphs into rock.

You can create your own fossil prints using play dough or clay and a variety of flat shapes or molds. Start by rolling the play dough out flat, then carefully press one side of your shape into the play dough to create an outline or mold fossil.

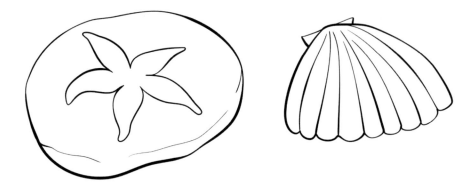

You can create a snail shell using play dough as well. Roll a lump of play dough into a long, thin cone. Carefully wrap the cone into a coil, starting at the narrow end.

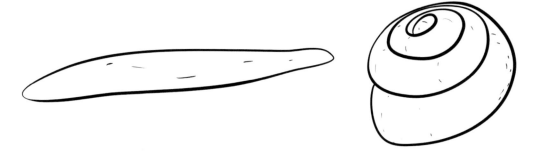

Pinch around the edges of the wide end to flare it out like the edges of a snail shell. You can also pinch the sides of the coil to create ridges, or you can flatten the coil a bit to change the shape of the snail shell. When you are happy with it, you can let it dry into a fossil, or take a few photos and then squash it up to make something new.

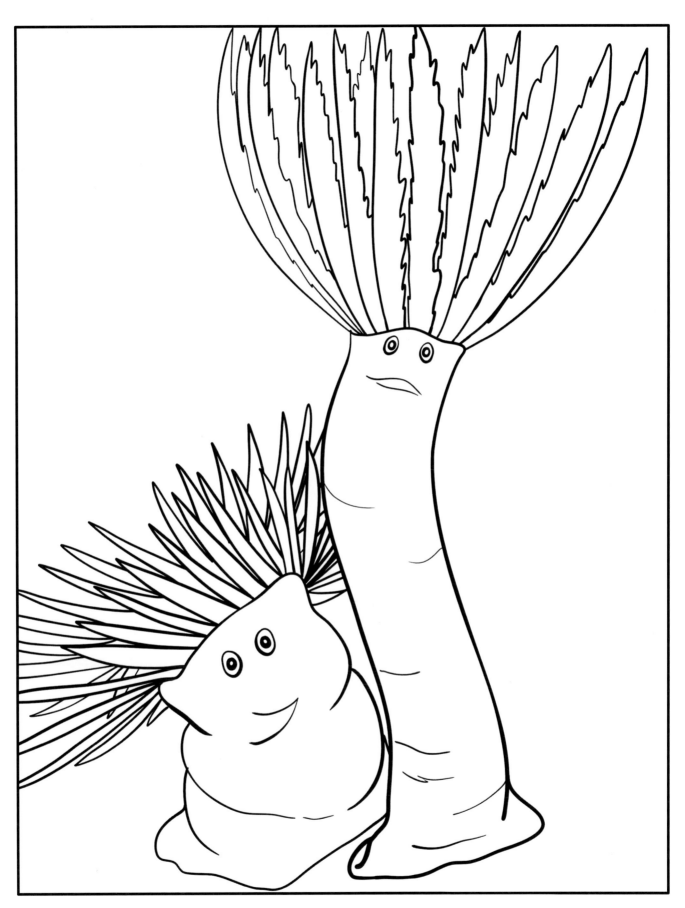

Do these feather duster worms look like sea anemones to you? They aren't related to sea anemones, but they are related to earthworms. Instead of crawling around in your garden, though, they filter food particles from seawater to eat.

Monkey in the Middle

Many marine invertebrates are sessile, meaning they sit in one place and only catch the food that comes close to them. This means they are a lot like the middle player in a game of Monkey in the Middle. In this version of the game, though, the food floats gently by in the water—rather like a cloud of bubbles.

To play, you need tape, bubbles, and two or more players, plus a leader.

Use tape to mark a square on the floor for each player. The squares can be grouped in a circle or scattered randomly across the floor. Have the players take their places in the squares. Once the players are ready, the leader should walk through the group scattering bubbles around the players. The players should try to catch as many of the bubbles as they can, without stepping outside their square.

Scoring:

For competitive scoring, have the players count how many bubbles they each caught. The one that caught the most bubbles wins, because they've captured the most food and will survive better than the other players.

Alternatively, have the players count how many bubbles they captured. If they captured more than five, they have gotten enough food to survive. If they captured less than five, they drop out of the game, and the remaining players take new positions to continue playing the game. This time, though, the players must catch ten bubbles. (*You can adjust the number of bubbles, as necessary.*)

For a non-competitive version of the game:

Have the players write down how many bubbles they each captured. Does it change depending on where they stand or how tall they are?

If all the players stand close together and the leader stays close to them, do they capture more bubbles? Or do they capture more bubbles when they are standing further apart, with the leader walking through the group?

Try playing another round of the game where the players can chase after the bubbles. Why do some animals stay in one place to capture food, while others travel around to find food? Which ones find more food? Which ones need more food?

What other experiments can the players try?

Can you guess what a bone-eating snot-flower worm eats? That's right—bones! These worms are tiny (less than an inch long), and they don't have any teeth. They use acid to dissolve the hard shell on bones to reach the nutrients inside.

Design Your Own Sea Creature

Thousands of different animals live in the ocean, from tiny plankton swimming along the surface to deep-sea worms living by hydrothermal vents. Here's your chance to design your own animal. Start by deciding where it will live and what it eats. How does it find its food? How would it protect itself?

Draw a picture of your animal here and come up with a name for it. Then check to see whether an animal like this really exists.

Sea spiders are not spiders. They look a lot like spiders—most sea spiders have eight legs—but they can't spin webs like a spider. Also, unlike regular spiders, sea spiders live in the ocean and absorb oxygen through their legs.

Many animals in this book—including crabs, shrimp, barnacles, and sea spiders—have external skeletons and jointed legs. This means that they are arthropods, just like spiders and insects. However, very few insects live in water. Even fewer live in saltwater. For example, this giant water bug lives in freshwater ponds, not the ocean. Use the grid below to finish drawing this insect, and then color the picture.

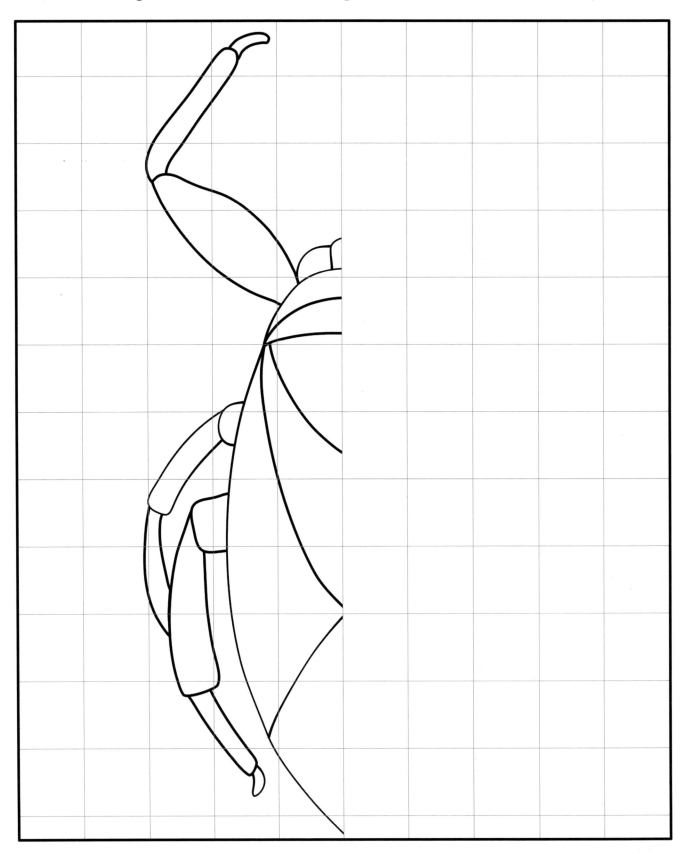